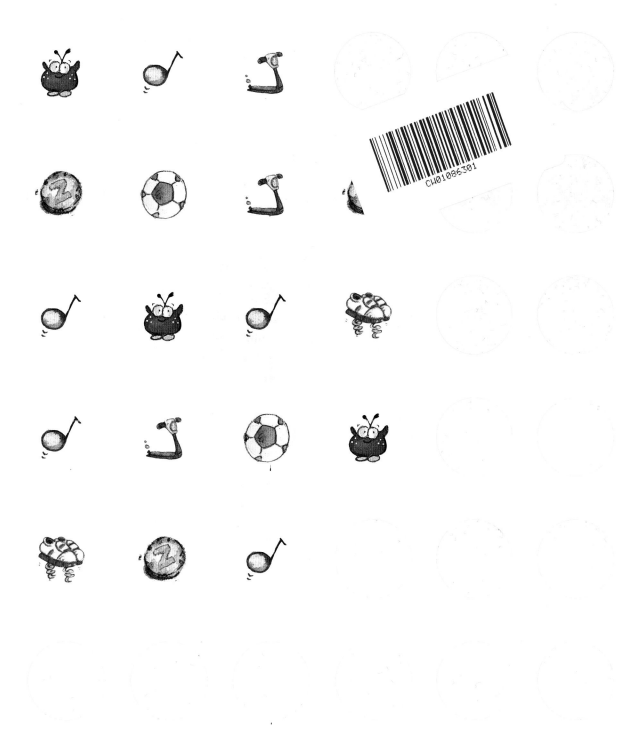

You think *you* have a long journey to school? Meet the Alien Club, a group of jolly aliens from the planet Dunk. They all entered a competition and won first prize – to go to school on planet Earth, six thousand light years away! Lucky their space-mobile runs on recycled rubbish and can travel a hundred light years in a heartbeat!

 Meet **Nok**, who finds football much easier than school, but tries all the same!

 Twinx, who loves ribbons, dancing and, her toy friend Mini T.

 Bouncing **Pogo**, who just cannot stand still!

 Pogo's pet dog, the rather less lively **Zen**, who will not get out of bed for less than a Z cookie or two.

 Zara P, zip zip zipping around on her scooter and making notes on everything she sees.

 And **Zing**, who loves his music most of all, but thinks school is pretty cool too!

Now the Alien Club want to pass on everything they have learnt to you. All you have to do is work your way through these tests and not only will you be the cleverest Earthling around, you will become a member of the Alien Club too! Out of this world!!!

English 6–7

Alison Head

Hello! I am Twinx and this is my toy friend Mini T. We love to dance! Dancing should be graceful and your handwriting should flow beautifully too. Joining your letters carefully helps you to write quickly and neatly.

See how neatly you can write over these words.

1 dance

2 fun

3 bounce

4 winter

5 shout

6 baby

7 little

8 old

9 where

10 other

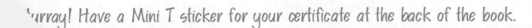

Alphabetical order

Hi there! I am Nok. I need to find information quickly, so I can finish my work and get back to playing football! That is why dictionaries and indexes are arranged in **alphabetical order** – to help you find things easily.

> Apple
>
> Banana
>
> Carrot

He shoots, he scores!

Write down which page these topics can be found on.

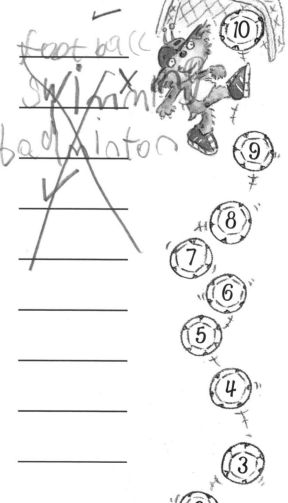

Index	Page
badminton	29
cricket	18
diving	6
football	12
golf	22
hockey	9
ice-skating	24
rugby	31
swimming	14
tennis	3

1 football _football_ ✓

2 swimming _swimming_ ✗

3 badminton _badminton_ ✗

4 golf _____ ✓

5 tennis _____

6 hockey _____

7 rugby _____

8 cricket _____

9 ice-skating _____

10 diving _____

Goal! Have a football sticker for your certificate at the back of the book.

Colour in score.

Hi, I am Pogo and I am always just a bounce away! Oi, watch out! I am coming through! Did you know, the **oy** sound can be made by the letters **oy** or **oi**, so you need to remember which one to use.

boy   coil

Circle the word which is spelt correctly in each pair.

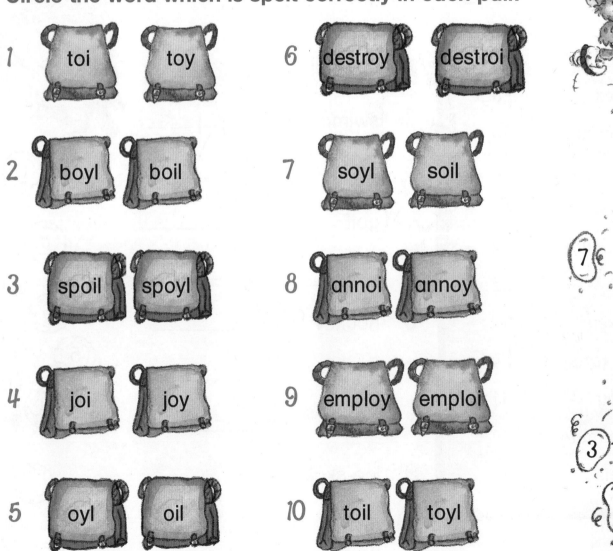

1 toi   toy

2 boyl   boil

3 spoil   spoyl

4 joi   joy

5 oyl   oil

6 destroy   destroi

7 soyl   soil

8 annoi   annoy

9 employ   emploi

10 toil   toyl

10 9 8 7 6 5 4 3 2 1

  Put a spring in your step! Have a springy sticker for your certificate.   Colour in your score.

Capital letters

Hi! Zara P, that is me, and I like to zip around on my scooter, making notes on what I find out along the way. I have just found out that **capital letters** go at the start of every sentence. You also need to use them for the names of people, places, days of the week and months.

Zara P   Dunk   Tuesday   March

Choose the correct word to complete each sentence.

1 My scooter goes really fast.

my	My

2 You will always find *Nok* playing football.

Nok	nok

3 We live on planet *dunk*.

dunk	Dunk

4 My favourite day is *Friday*.

friday	Friday

5 My birthday is in *April*.

April	april

6 When *I* find out something, I write it in my notebook.

i	I

7 Pogo *Bounces* all over the place.

Bounces	bounces

8 *Zing* is always listening to music.

zing	Zing

9 Twinx loves to practise *her* dancing.

her	Her

10 Z cookies keep *Zen* awake.

Zen	zen

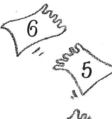

You are zippy! Have a scooter sticker for your certificate.

Colour in your score.

er sounds

Er, what? This is really tangling my antennae! Did you know, the **er** sound can be made in several ways, including **er**, **ir** and **ur**?

flow**er**   b**ir**d   p**ur**ple

If you practise, you will soon remember which letters to use for different words.

Choose er, ir or ur to complete each word.

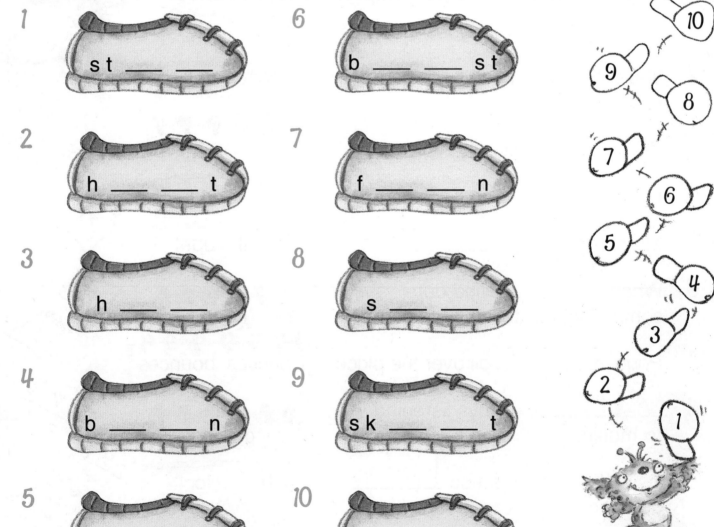

1 s t ___ ___

2 h ___ ___ t

3 h ___ ___

4 b ___ ___ n

5 d ___ ___ t

6 b ___ ___ s t

7 f ___ ___ n

8 s ___ ___

9 s k ___ ___ t

10 h ___ ___ d

Goal! Have a football sticker.

Colour in your score.

ed and ing

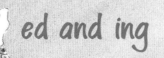

Hello there! I am Zen.
Watch**ing** my pal Pogo bounc**ing**
around makes me tired. Yesterday I
watch**ed** him until I fell asleep!

Verbs ending with **ed** show something
that happened in the past. Verbs
ending with **ing** show something that
is happening in the present.
I could do this in my… zzz.

Sort these words into past and present tense verbs.

1 eating

2 walked

3 listened

4 going

5 bouncing

6 pushed

7 writing

8 rushed

9 making

10 baked

_____

_____

_____

_____

_____

Past

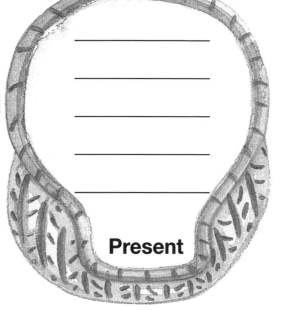

_____

_____

_____

_____

_____

Present

10
9
8
7
6
5
4
3
2
1

Well done! Have a Z cookie sticker.

Colour in your score.

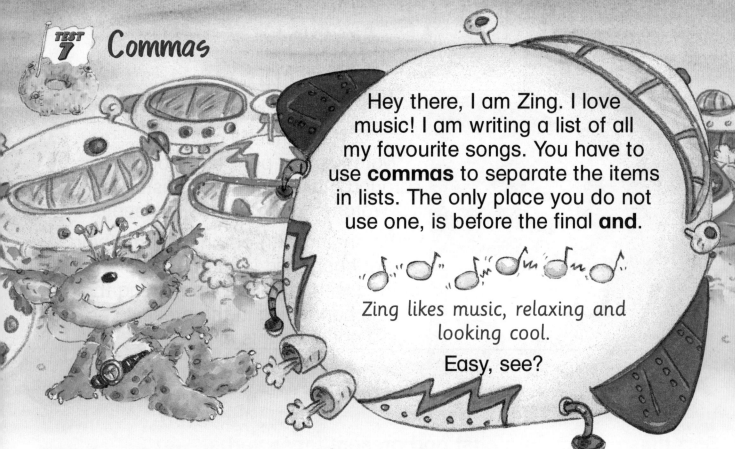

TEST 7 · Commas

Hey there, I am Zing. I love music! I am writing a list of all my favourite songs. You have to use **commas** to separate the items in lists. The only place you do not use one, is before the final **and**.

Zing likes music, relaxing and looking cool.

Easy, see?

Add the missing commas to these sentences.

1 You can see the Earth moon and stars from Dunk.

2 Zara P always has her notebook scooter pen and bag with her.

3 Nok loves his football trainers and baseball cap.

4 Twinx looks cute with her ribbons tutu ballet shoes and Mini T.

5 Zen is a lazy sleepy and hungry dog.

6 The Alien Club love maths English and science.

7 The space-mobile turns old paper cans and wrappers into fuel.

8 Pogo knows all about reading writing and spelling.

9 Mini T is small pretty and just like Twinx.

10 Nok Twinx Pogo Zen Zing and Zara P are the Alien Club.

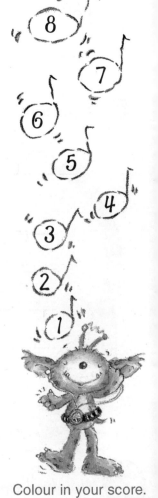

 Easy! Have a musical sticker.

Colour in your score.

Hurray! I love writing stories with Mini T. I often use **time words** like next and then to help me link my sentences together.

Nok played football. **Meanwhile***, Mini T and I danced.*

Underline 10 time words or phrases in this piece of writing.

At first, nobody realised that Zen was missing. Then Pogo noticed Zen had not eaten his cookies. Next, Zara P said she had not heard him snoring for a while. As a result, Twinx said they should look for him.

They searched high and low. During the search, Pogo found Nok's lost football boot. At the same time, Twinx found Zing's spare earphones and her favourite pink ribbon. After a while, their bedrooms were tidy!

Meanwhile, Zen had decided to come home. Before he could eat his cookies, he fell asleep. In the end, the gang found him snoring in his food bowl!

10 9 8 7 6 5 4 3 2 1

Hurray! Have a Mini T sticker.

Colour in your score.

When you ride a scooter, you have to be sure you are doing it right. **Instructions** tell you how to do things, but it is really important to get all the steps in the right order. Never fear, ZP is here!

Number these instructions 1–10 to put them in the right order.

Making a sandwich

 Slice the sandwich in half.

 Take out two slices of bread.

 Open the bread bag.

 Put the sliced sandwich on a plate.

 Enjoy your sandwich.

 Spread butter on one side of each slice of bread.

 Firstly, collect your bread, butter and choice of filling.

 Wash up the plate.

 Put the other slice on top, buttered side down.

 Add the topping to one of the buttered slices of bread.

 You are zippy! Have a scooter sticker.

Colour in your score.

TEST 10 — wh words

Boing, boing, boing! My springs make a lot of noise, unlike some of these letters, that do not make a sound at all! When words start with **wh**, you often cannot hear the **h**, so you have to remember when to add it.

w**h**ere   wail

Colour in the correctly spelt word in each pair.

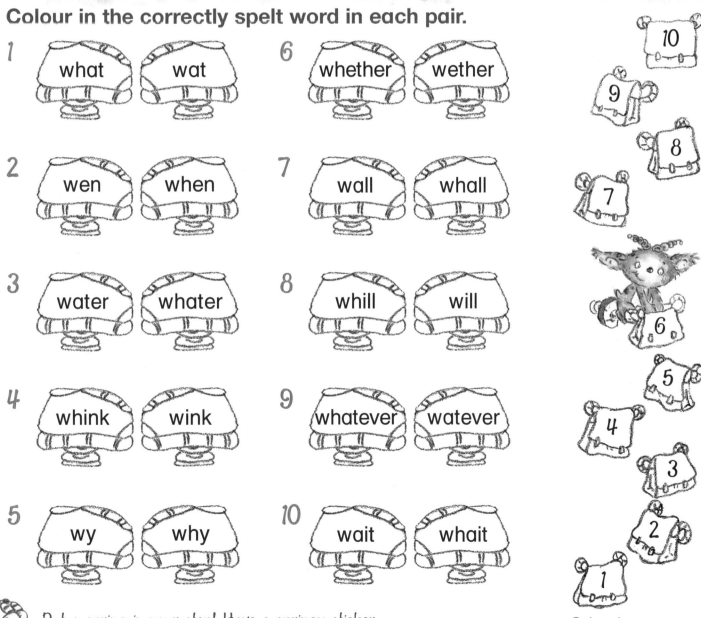

1 what / wat

2 wen / when

3 water / whater

4 whink / wink

5 wy / why

6 whether / wether

7 wall / whall

8 whill / will

9 whatever / watever

10 wait / whait

10 9 8 7 6 5 4 3 2 1

 Put a spring in your step! Have a springy sticker.

Colour in your score.

Earth words are amazing! Sometimes two words are joined together to make a new word. They are called **compound words**.

ear + phones = earphones

Breaking compound words up can help you spell them. Cool!

Write down the two words that have been joined together to make these compound words.

1 handbag

_____
_____

2 notebook

_____
_____

3 spaceman

_____
_____

4 football

_____
_____

5 homework

_____
_____

6 armchair

_____
_____

7 bookmark

_____
_____

8 hairbrush

_____
_____

9 shopkeeper

_____
_____

10 rainbow

_____
_____

Easy! Have a musical sticker.

Colour in your score.

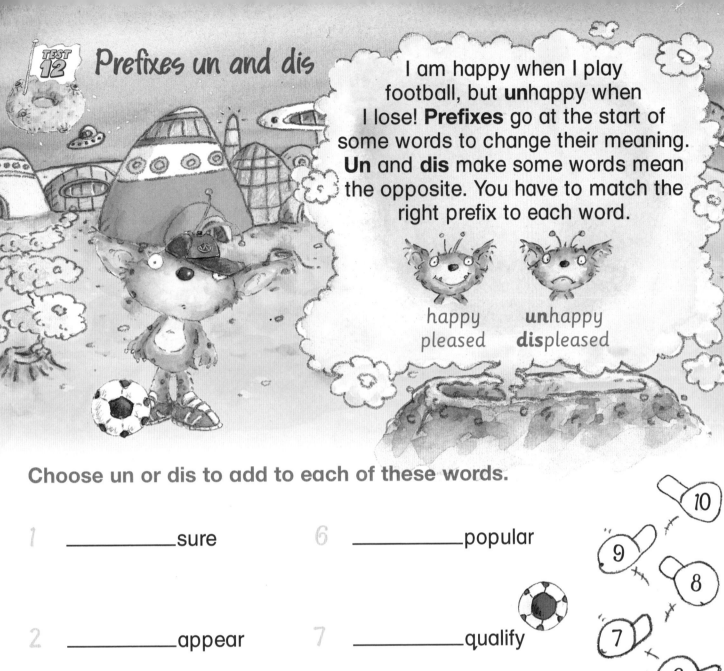

TEST 12 Prefixes un and dis

I am happy when I play football, but **un**happy when I lose! **Prefixes** go at the start of some words to change their meaning. **Un** and **dis** make some words mean the opposite. You have to match the right prefix to each word.

happy **un**happy
pleased **dis**pleased

Choose un or dis to add to each of these words.

1 _____sure

2 _____appear

3 _____honest

4 _____kind

5 _____obey

6 _____popular

7 _____qualify

8 _____tidy

9 _____agree

10 _____fortunate

 Goal! Have a football sticker.

Colour in your score.

Past tense verbs

I ate all my Z cookies! Ate is the past tense of the verb eat. We use **past tense verbs** for things that have already happened.

Lots of past tense verbs end with ed, but some have a special spelling.

Relax – you can do this!

Draw lines to join each word to its correct past tense form.

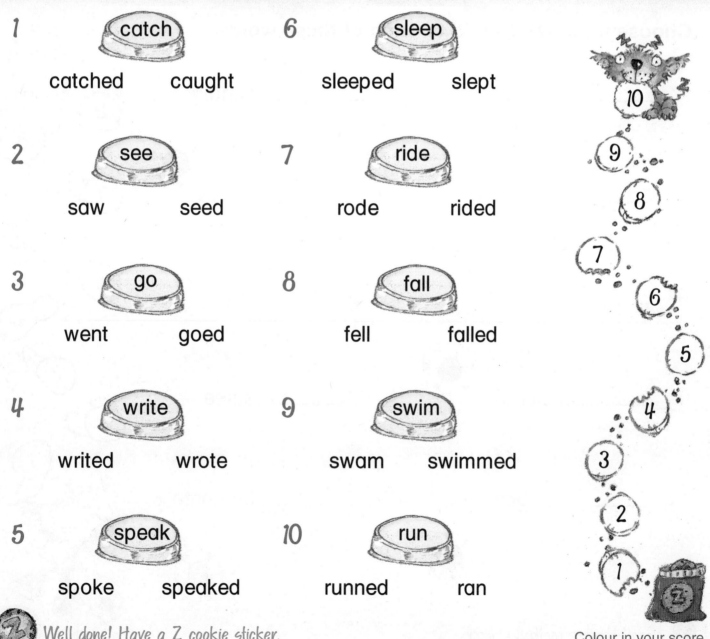

1 catch

catched   caught

2 see

saw   seed

3 go

went   goed

4 write

writed   wrote

5 speak

spoke   speaked

6 sleep

sleeped   slept

7 ride

rode   rided

8 fall

fell   falled

9 swim

swam   swimmed

10 run

runned   ran

10
9
8
7
6
5
4
3
2
1

Well done! Have a Z cookie sticker.

Colour in your score.

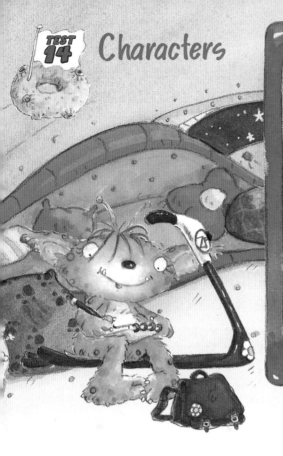

When I have read a story, I like to describe my favourite characters in my notebook. **Characters** are the people in stories. Writers describe them very carefully to bring them to life.

clever   whizzy

zippy

Zara P, that is me!

Read these character descriptions carefully, then decide which of the Alien Club members each one describes – Nok, Twinx, Pogo, Zen, Zara P or Zing.

1   He loves music.

2   She likes zipping about.

3   He often looks confused.

4   He is always bouncing around!

5   He sleeps a lot.

6   She has a toy friend.

7   He loves playing football.

8   She loves to dance.

9   She writes everything down.

10 He eats a lot of Z cookies.

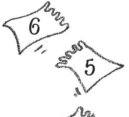
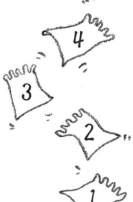

You are zippy! Have a scooter sticker.

Colour in your score.

Questions

Which ribbons should I wear? **Wh**at do you think, Mini T? Lots of **questions** seem to start with **wh** words!

what where when

why which who

Questions always finish with a question mark too.

Choose one word from the ribbons to complete each question.

1 Where   When   _____ is Pogo bouncing to?

2 Why   Which   _____ is Zen always asleep?

3 Who   Which   _____ alien loves to play football?

4 Who   What   _____ owns a jet scooter?

5 Which   What   _____ will the aliens learn at school today?

6 What   When   _____ does the space-mobile leave for Earth?

7 What   Where   _____ is Zing listening to?

8 Who   What   _____ does the space-mobile use as fuel?

9 Where   Which   _____ tutu will Twinx wear today?

10 Which   Who   _____ wears a baseball cap?

Hurray! Have a Mini T sticker.

Colour in your score.

Suffixes ful and ly

Good football is all about being skil**ful** and playing bold**ly**. You can add **suffixes ful** and **ly** to the ends of some words to change their meaning. Often you can just add them, but if the word ends in a consonant followed by **y**, you change it to **i** first. Get it? Goal!

Complete these word sums. Remember the spelling rule for adding suffixes to words ending with y.

1 shame + ful = _____

2 happy + ly = _____

3 lazy + ly = _____

4 bold + ly = _____

5 hope + ful = _____

6 play + ful = _____

7 pretty + ly = _____

8 quick + ly = _____

9 duty + ful = _____

10 doubt + ful = _____

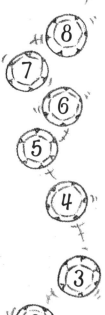

Goal! Have a football sticker.

Colour in your score.

Zen is always ready for a Z cookie, or a nap! It is a shame spelling is not so reliable. The same word sounds can often be spelt in different ways. Like the **air** sound:

p**air**   st**are**   b**ear**   wh**ere**

Zen would need a lot of Z cookies to get through this one!

Sort these words into the correct rucksack, depending on how the 'air' sound is spelt.

1	fair	*2*	scare	*3*	wear	*4*	hair
5	pear	*6*	tear	*7*	care	*8*	rare
9	spare	*10*	stairs				

air

_____

_____

_____

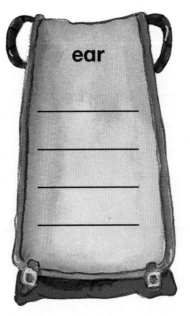

ear

_____

_____

_____

_____

are

_____

_____

_____

_____

Put a spring in your step! Have a springy sticker.

Colour in your score.

Making notes

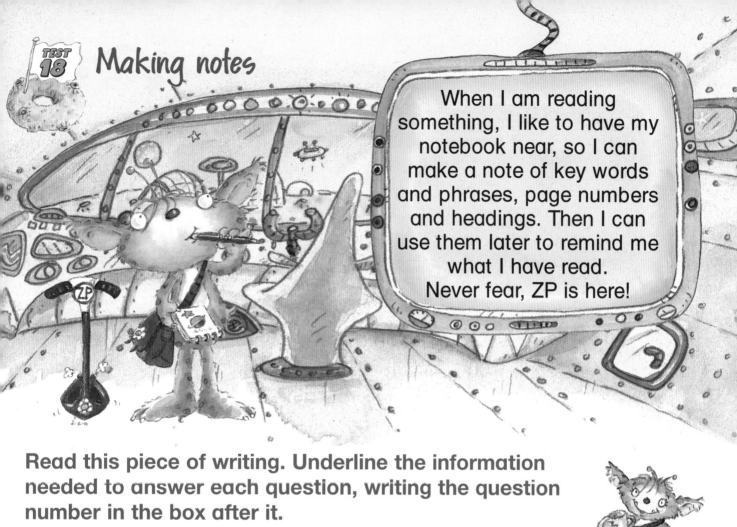

When I am reading something, I like to have my notebook near, so I can make a note of key words and phrases, page numbers and headings. Then I can use them later to remind me what I have read.
Never fear, ZP is here!

Read this piece of writing. Underline the information needed to answer each question, writing the question number in the box after it.

Jet-scooters ☐ By X Zeban ☐ Page 8 ☐

Jet-scooters can reach speeds of 30 miles per hour ☐. They are powered by space rocks ☐ and can travel for three miles ☐ on one rock. The Saturn 4 ☐ model is the most popular, and is available in pink and blue ☐. Because it can fly outside the atmosphere of Dunk ☐, riders must be at least 10 years old ☐.

1 How far can a jet-scooter go on one space rock?

2 What page is it on?

3 How old must riders be?

4 How are jet-scooters powered?

5 What is the most popular model?

6 What is the heading for the piece of writing?

7 How fast can a jet-scooter go?

8 What colours are available?

9 Where can a jet-scooter fly?

10 Who wrote the piece of writing?

 You are zippy! Have a scooter sticker.

Colour in your score.

Synonyms

Yuck! It is hard to describe how bad that rubbish smells. What do you think, Mini T?

pongy   smelly   stinky

Words like this, with similar meanings, are called **synonyms**. They are clever, because they save you having to use the same word too often. Hurray!

Think of an interesting synonym for these words.

1   small

   _____

2   big

   _____

3   wet

   _____

4   hungry

   _____

5   tired

   _____

6   sad

   _____

7   quick

   _____

8   cold

   _____

9   hot

   _____

10   pretty

   _____

9 10 8 7 6 5 4 3 2 1

Hurray! Have a Mini T sticker!   Colour in your score.

Antonyms

All my music is brilliant, but some music is dreadful! When two words have opposite meanings, they are called **antonyms**.

loud   quiet

Antonyms are useful for describing the differences between things. Cool!

Think of an antonym for these words.

1 lost _____

2 high _____

3 early _____

4 fast _____

5 full _____

6 top _____

7 above _____

8 cold _____

9 pretty _____

10 hard _____

10 9 8 7 6 5 4 3 2 1

Easy! Have a musical sticker.

Colour in your score.

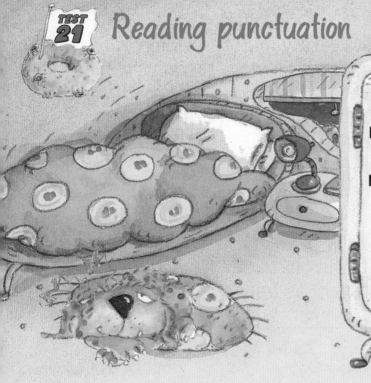

I always like to pause between naps for a Z cookie or two. When you are reading, punctuation marks like commas and full stops tell you how long to pause. Exclamation marks show that something exciting is happening.

Relax – you can do this!

Decide what the blue punctuation tells you about how to read each sentence. Then join each sentence to the correct planet.

1 Look at the shooting star!

2 After school, Twinx plays with Mini T.

3 The space-mobile flies through the Milky Way.

4 The aliens play in the craters.

5 Nok has scored a goal!

6 The space-mobile is ready to leave.

7 Because of his springs, Pogo bounces everywhere.

8 Looking in her bag, Zara P found her notebook.

9 Zoom! There goes Zara P on her scooter.

10 Zing listens to music, because he loves it.

Take a short pause in your reading.

Take a longer pause – the sentence has finished.

Use lots of expression – something exciting is happening.

10
9
8
7
6
5
4
3
2
1

 Well done! Have a Z cookie sticker.

Colour in your score.

Present tense verbs

Oh dear, Mini T! Choosing the right part of **present tense verbs** is tricky! I dance, but Mini T dances. Dance is a verb and the part of present tense verbs you use often depends on who you are talking about.

I skip   she skips   they skip

Circle the correct verb in each sentence.

1   I   am   is   tired.

2   He   runs   run   fast.

3   We   eat   eats   pizza.

4   They   am   are   late.

5   She   go   goes   to school.

6   It   is   am   dark.

7   We   play   plays   cricket.

8   He   learn   learns   quickly.

9   You   read   reads   a book.

10   They   walks   walk   to school.

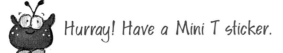

Hurray! Have a Mini T sticker.

Colour in your score.

I used to find it difficult to tell when a character in a book was speaking, until I discovered **speech marks**! They go at the beginning and end of what a character says, so you know who is saying what.

"He shoots, he scores!" yelled Nok.

He shoots, he scores!

Find the speech in these sentences and copy it into the speech bubbles.

1   "Look at me!" laughed Twinx.

2   "I am so sleepy!" yawned Zen.

3   Zara P said, "That is interesting."

4   Zing said, "Turn up the music!"

5   "Goal!" shouted Nok.

6   "Where is my Mini T?" asked Twinx.

7   Pogo said, "I love bouncing!"

8   "The space-mobile is here!" cried the aliens.

9   Zen asked, "Is that a Z cookie?"

10   Zing said, "I will help you."

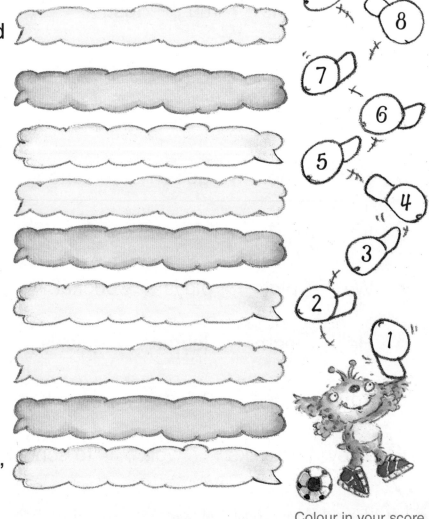

Goal! Have a football sticker.

Colour in your score.

Special effects

Too much plain text is just not cool! Key words in boxes , **bold**, <u>underlined</u> or *italics*, really stand out. Or make them bigger, smaller, put them in CAPITALS or a different colour.

Try speech bubbles and picture captions too. Cool, huh?

Aliens at the beach

Write down which special effect is being used in each sentence, using the words in the box to help you.

boxed text	underlined	bold text	smaller text
coloured text	bigger text	speech bubble	
italics	picture caption	capital letters	

1. The aliens live on planet <u>Dunk</u>. _____

2. Zing plays his music very **loudly**. _____

3. Pogo can bounce because of his **springs**. _____

4. Let's dance! _____

5. Special effects make words *stand out*. _____

6. _____

   A space-mobile

7. Zara P loves her NOTEBOOK and PEN. _____

8. Z cookies make Zen wake up. _____

9. The Alien Club love school. _____

10. Mini T is really tiny. _____

Easy! Have a musical sticker.

Colour in your score.

Boing, boing, boing! I just love the sound my springs make! Sometimes in words, though, the same sound can be spelt in different ways. Like the **or** sound:

p**or**t   p**oo**r   m**or**e   s**aw**

It is enough to make you hopping mad!

Circle the correctly spelt word on each spring.

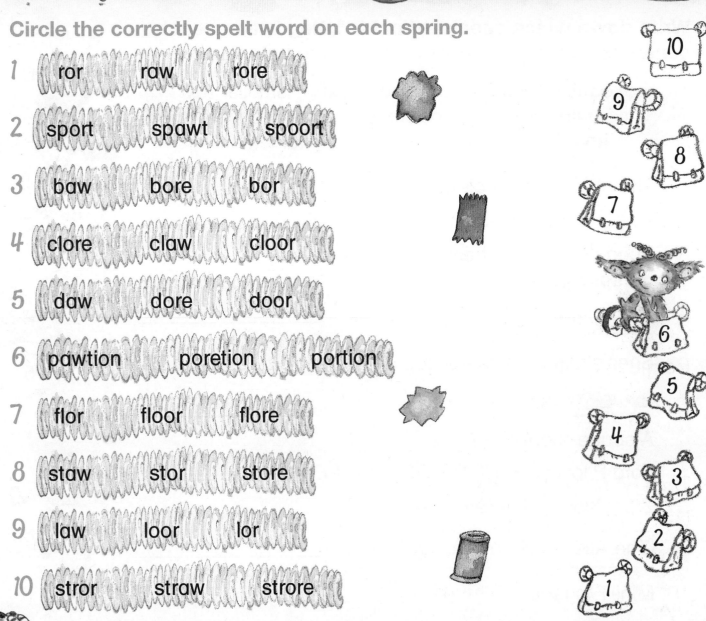

1 ror   raw   rore

2 sport   spawt   spoort

3 baw   bore   bor

4 clore   claw   cloor

5 daw   dore   door

6 pawtion   poretion portion

7 flor   floor   flore

8 staw   stor   store

9 law   loor   lor

10 stror   straw   strore

Put a spring in your step! Have a springy sticker.

Colour in your score.

Mini T loves words that rhyme, because she thinks they sound pretty. Lots of poems have rhyming words at the ends of the lines.

I love to play with **Mini T**,
She is the perfect friend for **me**.
What do you think, Mini T?

Finish the poem, using the words in the rocket to help you. Remember, the words rhyme in pairs. Some letters have been filled in for you.

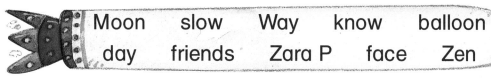

Moon   slow   Way   know   balloon
day   friends   Zara P   face   Zen

Take a rocket into space,
Feel the starlight on your __ __ __ __.
Zoom around the smiling M __ __ __,
Like a grinning white b __ __ __ __ __ n.

Go for a moon walk, floating s __ __ __.
It's made of stinky cheese, you __ __ __ __!
Zoom around the Milky W __ __,
It gets more milky every __ __ __.

Then on to Dunk to meet the f __ __ __ __ __ __ __.
Nok, Zing and sleepy Z __ __,
Twinx, Pogo, Z __ __ __ __,
The coolest gang in history!

Hurray! Have a Mini T sticker.

Colour in your score.

I am pretending I am the hero in a football story, about to score the winning goal. Imagine – the huge stadium, roar of the crowd...

Well-described settings are very important in stories, because they help to bring the story to life. He shoots, he scores!

See if you can imagine what Dunk's neighbouring planet, Zamen, looks like. Include these descriptions in a drawing.

1 Red craters are dotted about.

2 The sky is green.

3 The planet has two moons.

4 Cars on Zamen have no wheels and hover above the ground.

5 The buildings are shaped like huge witches' hats.

6 There are mountains, topped with green snow.

7 Many space craft fill the sky.

8 The aliens on Zamen are blue, with very long arms.

9 They have one huge eye.

10 The trees have pink leaves.

Goal! Have a football sticker.

Syllables

Pogo will break something if he is not careful! Have you noticed that lots of words can be broken up into chunks, or beats, when you say them?

coo   kie

These beats are called **syllables** and they give a word its rhythm.

Read each of these words out loud, then write how many syllables it has on the Z cookie.

1 Pogo

2 Zing

3 Dunk

4 Twinx

5 Zen

6 scooter

7 space

8 alien

9 planet

10 universe

10
9
8
7
6
5
4
3
2
1

 Congratulations! Have a last Z cookie sticker for your certificate. Good work!

Colour in your score.

Answers

Test 1 Handwriting
Words should be traced carefully and accurately.

Test 2 Alphabetical order
1 Page 12
2 Page 14
3 Page 29
4 Page 22
5 Page 3
6 Page 9
7 Page 31
8 Page 18
9 Page 24
10 Page 6

Test 3 oy sounds
The correctly spelt words are:
1 toy
2 boil
3 spoil
4 joy
5 oil
6 destroy
7 soil
8 annoy
9 employ
10 toil

Test 4 Capital letters
Words needed to complete the sentences are:
1 My
2 Nok
3 Dunk
4 Friday
5 April
6 I
7 bounces
8 Zing
9 her
10 Zen

Test 5 er sounds
1 stir
2 hurt
3 her
4 burn
5 dirt
6 burst
7 fern
8 sir
9 skirt
10 herd

Test 6 ed and ing
Past tense verbs are:
walked, listened, pushed, rushed, baked.

Present tense verbs are:
eating, going, bouncing, writing, making.

Test 7 Commas
1 You can see the Earth, moon and stars from Dunk.
2 Zara P always has her notebook, scooter, pen and bag with her.
3 Nok loves his football, trainers and baseball cap.
4 Twinx looks cute with her ribbons, tutu, ballet shoes and Mini T.
5 Zen is a lazy, sleepy and hungry dog.
6 The Alien Club love maths, English and science.
7 The space-mobile turns old paper, cans and wrappers into fuel.
8 Pogo knows all about reading, writing and spelling.
9 Mini T is small, pretty and just like Twinx.
10 Nok, Twinx, Pogo, Zen, Zing and Zara P are the Alien Club.

Test 8 Time words
<u>At first</u>, nobody realised that Zen was missing. <u>Then</u> Pogo noticed that Zen had not eaten his cookies. <u>Next</u>, Zara P said she had not heard him snoring for a while. <u>As a result</u>, Twinx said they should look for him.

They searched high and low. <u>During</u> the search, they found Nok's lost football boot. <u>At the same time</u>, Twinx found Zing's spare earphones and her favourite pink ribbon. <u>After a while</u>, their bedrooms were tidy!

<u>Meanwhile</u>, Zen had decided to come home. <u>Before</u> he could eat his cookies, he fell asleep. <u>In the end</u>, the gang found him snoring <u>in his</u> food bowl!

Test 9 Instructions
The correct order is:
1 Firstly, collect your bread, butter and choice of filling.
2 Open the bread bag.
3 Take out two slices of bread.
4 Spread butter on one side of each slice of bread.
5 Add the topping to one of the buttered slices of bread.
6 Put the other slice on top, buttered side down.
7 Slice the sandwich in half.
8 Put the sliced sandwich on a plate.
9 Enjoy your sandwich.
10 Wash up the plate.

Test 10 wh words
The correctly spelt words are:
1 what
2 when
3 water
4 wink
5 why
6 whether
7 wall
8 will
9 whatever
10 wait

Test 11 Compound words
1 hand bag
2 note book
3 space man
4 foot ball
5 home work
6 arm chair
7 book mark
8 hair brush
9 shop keeper
10 rain bow

Test 12 Prefixes un and dis
1 unsure
2 disappear
3 dishonest
4 unkind
5 disobey
6 unpopular
7 disqualify
8 untidy
9 disagree
10 unfortunate

Test 13 Past tense verbs
The correct past tense forms are:
1. caught
2. saw
3. went
4. wrote
5. spoke
6. slept
7. rode
8. fell
9. swam
10. ran

Test 14 Characters
1. Zing
2. Zara P
3. Nok
4. Pogo
5. Zen
6. Twinx
7. Nok
8. Twinx
9. Zara P
10. Zen

Test 15 Questions
1. **Where** is Pogo bouncing to?
2. **Why** is Zen always asleep?
3. **Which** alien loves to play football?
4. **Who** owns a jet-scooter?
5. **What** will the aliens learn today?
6. **When** does the space-mobile leave for Earth?
7. **What** is Zing listening to?
8. **What** does the space-mobile use as fuel?
9. **Which** tutu will Twinx wear today?
10. **Who** wears a baseball cap?

Test 16 Suffixes ful and ly
1. shameful
2. happily
3. lazily
4. boldly
5. hopeful
6. playful
7. prettily
8. quickly
9. dutiful
10. doubtful

Test 17 air sounds
air words: fair, hair, stairs

ear words: wear, pear, tear

are words: scare, care, rare, spare

Test 18 Making notes
1. three miles
2. Page 8
3. at least 10 years old
4. by space rocks
5. Saturn 4
6. Jet scooters
7. 30 miles per hour
8. pink and blue
9. outside the atmosphere of Dunk
10. X Zeban

Test 19 Synonyms
Many answers are possible, but strong answers may include:
1. tiny, little
2. huge, massive
3. damp, dripping
4. starving, peckish
5. exhausted, sleepy
6. unhappy, miserable
7. fast, speedy
8. chilly, freezing
9. warm, scorching
10. beautiful, cute

Test 20 Antonyms
Many answers are possible, but strong answers may include:
1. found
2. low
3. late
4. slow
5. empty
6. bottom
7. below
8. hot
9. ugly
10. soft

Test 21 Reading punctuation
Take a short pause in your reading: 2, 7, 8, 10

Take a longer pause – the sentence has finished: 3, 4, 6

Use lots of expression – something exciting is happening: 1, 5, 9

Test 22 Present tense verbs
1. I (am) tired.
2. He (runs) fast
3. We (eat) pizza.
4. They (are) late.
5. She (goes) to school.
6. It (is) dark.
7. We (play) cricket.
8. He (learns) quickly.
9. You (read) a book.
10. They (walk) to school.

Test 23 Speech marks
1. Look at me!
2. I am so sleepy!
3. That is interesting.
4. Turn up the music!
5. Goal!
6. Where is my Mini T?
7. I love bouncing!
8. The space-mobile is here!
9. Is that a Z cookie?
10. I will help you.

Test 24 Special effects
1. underlined
2. bigger text
3. bold text
4. speech bubble
5. italics
6. picture caption
7. capital letters
8. coloured text
9. boxed text
10. smaller text

Test 25 or sounds
The correctly spelt words are:
1. raw
2. sport
3. bore
4. claw
5. door
6. portion
7. floor
8. store
9. law
10. straw

Test 26 Rhyme in poetry
Take a rocket into space,
Feel the starlight on your **face**.
Zoom around the smiling **moon**,
Like a grinning white **balloon**.

Go for a moon walk, floating **slow**.
It's made of stinky cheese, you **know**!
Zoom around the Milky **Way**,
It gets more milky every **day**.

Then on to Dunk to meet the **friends**.
Nok, Zing and sleepy **Zen**,
Twinx, Pogo, **Zara P**,
The coolest gang in history!

Test 27 Setting the scene
The completed picture should include all features described.

Test 28 Syllables
1. 2
2. 1
3. 1
4. 1
5. 1
6. 2
7. 1
8. 3
9. 2
10. 3

Alien Club Certificate

Congratulations, _____, from everyone on planet Dunk!
You have collected all your award stickers and are now a member of the
English 6-7 Alien Club.
You are out of this world!

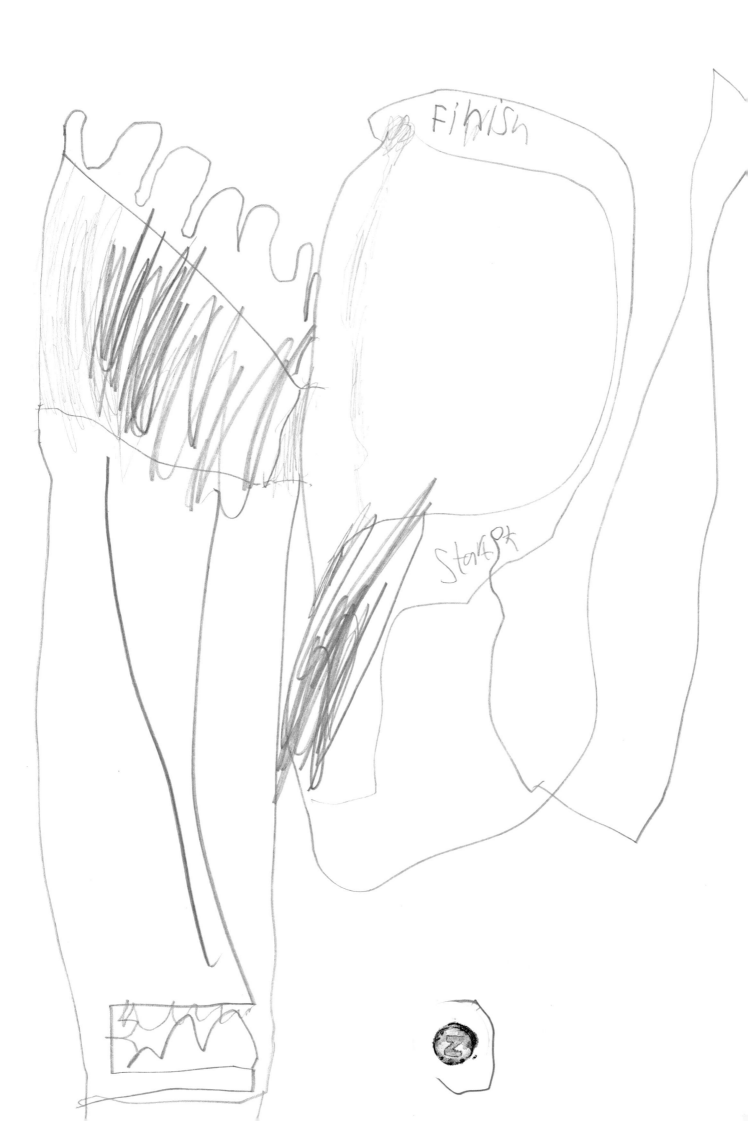

Finish

Start pt